SURPRISING USES FOR

ALLAN PLENDERLEITH

RAVETTE PUBLISHING

First published in 2018
by
Ravette Publishing Limited
PO Box 876, Horsham, West Sussex RH12 9GH
info@ravettepub.co.uk

ISBN: 978-1-84161-408-3

Printed in India by Imprint Press

For Becky

xxx

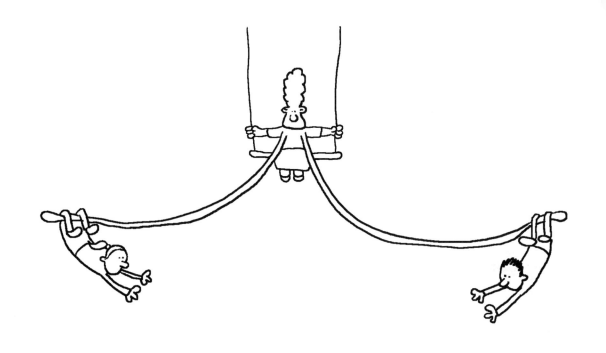

Also available by Allan Plenderleith:

ISBN: 978-1-84161-335-2